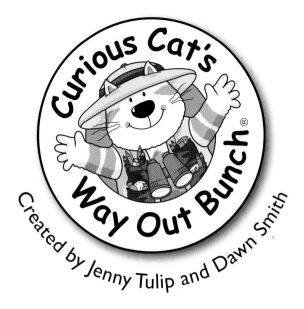

Created by Jenny Tulip and Dawn Smith

Curious Cat's Way Out Bunch books feature
endangered and vulnerable living animals.
The information in each book is gathered
from known facts about them.

Research by Simon Greenaway.

With special thanks to Gray Jolliffe for all his help and encouragement.

I'm Curious Cat on an adventure to see,
What the animal within these pages can be.
So let's read together and have a good look
And we shall find out by the end of this book.

The World

Kenya

Curious Cat is off to explore Kenya in Africa.
'Help me choose the Kenyan flag
and I will wear it on my hat.'

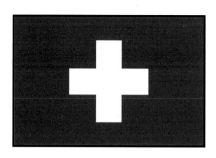

Switzerland

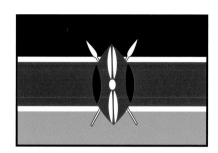

Kenya

Canada

Greece

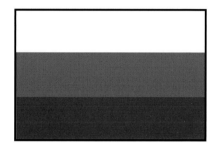

Russia

United Arab Emirates

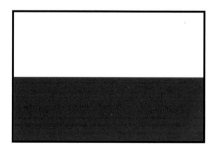

Poland

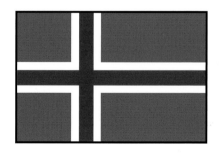

Iceland

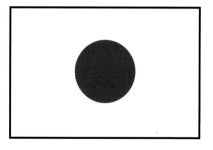

Japan

My splendid long nose is constantly quivering,
Seeking bugs, grubs and worms
That are scuttling and wriggling.

My two glittering eyes are round and bright,
I can see all about, I have very good sight.

'I wonder what on earth this animal is?
Do you think it can be one of these?'

My little bald ears can hear every sound,
They alert me to predators lurking around.

My four skinny legs look spindly and long,
When I need to move quickly
They're fast and they're strong.

'I wonder what this animal likes to eat.
Can you remember?'

Wherever I feed a small bird can be found,
Looking for titbits I leave on the ground.

I build little nests to sleep in at night,
Where I run to and hide when avoiding a fight.

Can you find me?

'In Kenya where this animal lives
there are many other creatures too.
I wonder if you have spotted some of them.'

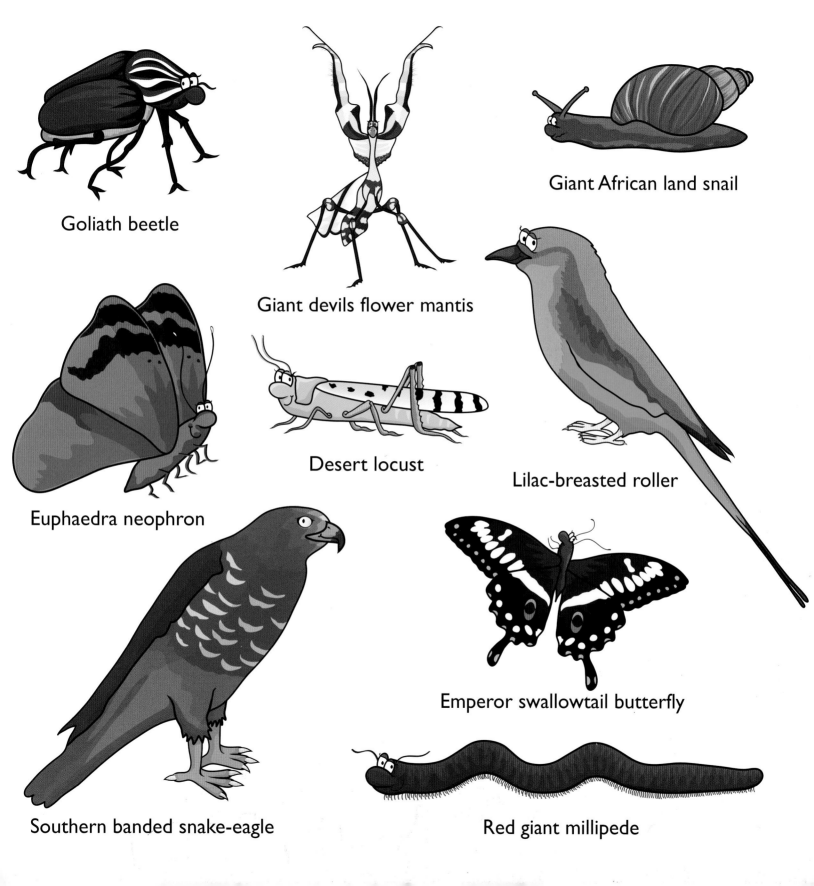

Goliath beetle

Giant devils flower mantis

Giant African land snail

Euphaedra neophron

Desert locust

Lilac-breasted roller

Southern banded snake-eagle

Emperor swallowtail butterfly

Red giant millipede

The fur on my bottom is the colour of gold,
And my long white-tipped tail is a sight to behold.

'This little creature is odd to see,
Have you guessed what it can be?'

I'm called a Golden-rumped elephant-shrew
And I'd just like to say, 'How do you do?'

Did you know.....

Humans, including you, can run quite fast, some athletes as fast as 48kph. The Golden-rumped elephant-shrew/sengi can run at speeds of up to 25kph, and if you consider it is only the size of a small rabbit, that's very fast indeed.

When threatened by a predator such as a snake or bird of prey, they will often slap the ground with their tail to distract them. If this doesn't work, they can quickly run away and escape.

The skin on their bottom is extra thick to prevent them from biting attacks when fighting with other shrews.

They eat mainly small insects including spiders, beetles, earthworms and millipedes.

As the Golden-rumped elephant-shrew/sengi feeds, a little bird called the Red-capped Robin-chat often follows eating any left over food.

Golden-rumped elephant-shrews/sengi live for between 4 and 5 years.

They build several nests to sleep in, made of leaves and grass and can use a different one every night.

Golden-rumped elephant-shrew/sengi are most closely related to elephants, aardvarks and dugongs, (a large marine mammal).

They live within a small area of deciduous coastal forest, some of which is included within the Arabuko-Sokoke National Park near Mombasa in Kenya, East Africa.

They are endangered because they are unable to climb or burrow making them vulnerable to predators.

Farmers are encroaching into the small area of deciduous coastal forest that is their remaining habitat.

If you would like to find out more information on endangered animals and how to help them, visit these websites:

WWF-UK - www.wwf.org.uk
The Edge programme - www.edgeofexistence.org
ARKive, images of life on Earth - www.arkive.org
Photographer - Galen Rathbun